Super Dad

Written by Roderick Hunt
Illustrated by Alex Brychta

OXFORD
UNIVERSITY PRESS

4

"Look at Dad," said Mum.

"Dad looks silly," said Wilma.

"No, he looks good," said
Wilf.

Dad put on a red nose.

"Oh no!" said Wilma.

"Dad looks so silly."

Dad had a bucket.

"Put your coins in here,"
he said.

Oh no! A man took Dad's bucket.

"Stop!" called Mum. "Come back."

But the man did not stop.

Dad got on a bike.

The man ran fast . . .

but Dad was faster.

"Got you," said Dad.

"Help!" said the man.

"Super Dad!" said Wilma.

Talk about the story

A maze

Help Dad to catch the thief.